Thirty Paths to Meditate

Thirty Paths To Meditate is the fourth in the
companion set. This selection of meditations,
visualisations and breathing techniques will
take your students on a journey to relaxation.

They have been tried and tested on my own
students, therefore Thirty Paths is dedicated to
all those who are continually seeking that still
small voice within, that which is within us all.

Om Shanti.

Susan Johnson
September 2007

Thirty Paths to Meditate

Index of Photographs

Inside Cover Lake Louise, Canadian Rockies

2	Spirit Island, Maligne Lake, Jasper, Canada
7	Uig, Lewis and Harris, Outer Hebrides
11	Derwentwater, Lake District
13	Toe Head, Outer Hebrides
21	Rodel Point, Harris Outer Hebrides
25	Harrison Stickle, Lake District.
28	Lewis and Harris
31	Canadian Rockies
33	David's Allotment
35	Lewis and Harris
37	Lewis and Harris
38	Susan's Grandparents
41	Uig, Lewis and Harris
46	Elterwater, Lake District
47	Athabaska Falls, Canadian Rockies
48	The Bow River, Canadian Rockies

Written and devised by Susan Johnson

Designed by The Art Room
Some Photography by David Johnson

Printed in England by CP Offset Limited, Darlington.
Telephone 01325 462315
e-mail: print@cpoffset.co.uk
First printed and published October 2007

Published by Susan Johnson
© Susan Johnson 2007
E-mail: susan@thirtypaths.com
website: www.thirtypaths.com

Printed on ecologically friendly sustainable stock

Contents

4	Yoga Nidra.
6	A Path To Stillness
8	Breathing In a Rainbow.
10	Drawing down The Moon.
12	Fields of Colour.
14	Walking in Meditation.
15	Affirmations with a Posture
16	Lesson Plan on The Four Elements.
18	The White Feather.
19	The Ocean of Dreams.
20	The Silent Glen.
22	The Tree of Life.
24	The Oasis
25	Mountain Meditation
26	Candle Meditation
28	Silence by the sea
29	Clearing the mind
30	The River.
32	The Summer Show.
34	The Changing Sky
36	The Boat Trip
38	Love yourself
39	The Healing Room
40	Meditating on Aum
42	Letting Go Of Today
43	Rapid Visualisation
44	Chakra Meditation
46	Four Seasons in the woods.
47	The Rainbow Pool
48	Christmas Meditation

Yoga Nidra

Yoga Nidra precedes visualisation. Before we start to imagine, the body must be totally relaxed. Begin the relaxation technique by allowing the body to totally let go.

Feel the body sinking into the mat, allow the shoulders to spread across the floor, move the head from side to side to release the neck, allow the head to let go. Imagine a cool blue light surrounding your body from the crown of the head to the tips of the toes, feel this light widening outwards, creating an aura of light around you. Feel it pulsating with life and energy, allow this light to be a healing light, if you feel in need of healing either mentally, emotionally, or physically allow this healing to take place whilst you relax.

Take the attention to the breath and allow the belly to slowly rise and fall with each breath, do not try and alter the breath in any way just witness the in and out, the flow, the slow coming and going, the evenness, the quiet rhythm. Allow the body to just be.

Now you are aware of melting down onto the floor, and you feel quite safe and secure,feel the colour blue soaking into the body, drenching all your cells with fresh life force, with energy, with balance, allow yourself to surrender to the healing.

Now take the attention to the feet, and allow the toes to spread and separate. Turn the toes inwards, flex and release, allow the instep to let go, the sole of the foot, the

ankle, and feel the feet as solid and heavy, feel as though the feet are moving away from you, dense and heavy so heavy that you feel as though you are unable to move them. Allow the feet to relax and let go, feel them flopping out to the side. Allow the legs to release, the shins, the calfs, the knee and the kneecap, the thigh and the back of the thigh allow the legs to release and let go, feel as though the legs are moving away from you solid, heavy and dense. Take the attention to the hands, to the back of the hand touching the floor, to the fingertips, the fingers and the palm of the hand, feel the softness in the palm of the hand, allow the lower arm to let go, the elbow, the upper arm, the whole of the arm releasing down, moving away.

Take the attention to the back and feel the vertebrae release from the base of the spine to the crown of the head visualise each vertebrae letting go and release onto the floor. Feel the whole of the back spread outwards, feel the back widen,at the same time feel the length, the stretch, the whole of the back spreading across the floor, and be aware of the amount of space the body takes up, the small amount of space.

Take the visualisation to the belly and be aware of the softness in the belly, the slow steady breath, the calm quiet coming and going of the breath, witness the rhythm, the separation of the breath, the pause, and the still point, feel as if the whole body is

reathing, that the breath is breathing the
ody.

llow the abdomen to let go and feel the
oftness in the
elly, allow
ne chest
entre to
pen out and
n each
halation feel
ne division of
ne breath,
low this
penness to
eate a space
ithin the
nest centre
lowing you
e freedom
o breathe
entally and
nysically,
low this
eedom to
pen out the
eart centre

As ...... to let go and soften,
the lower jaw
slightly drops,
feel the entire
face release,
the forehead,
the eyes, the
eyebrows, the
eyelids
relaxing in
pools of
darkness, the
temples, the
nose, the tip
of the nose,
the cheeks,
the
cheekbones,
the upper lip
and the lower
lip, the jaw
and the hinges
of the jaw, the

eating a releasement, a feeling you may not
ave felt for a long time, allow this centre to
e filled with peace.

el this openness now spreading to the
roat to release the voice, to move around
ne neck, the back of the head, the crown of

chin and even the ears and earlobes.

Feel the whole body release and sink down
onto the floor all you are aware of is the
steady breath, the rise and fall of the belly as
the breath moves in and out, the stillness, the
journey to visualisation.

5

A Path to Stillness

Imagine you are walking along a sandy pathway, towards the beach. The sand dunes are high, hiding the seashore. The path meanders in and out; wild flowers are in abundance, sand snails cling to the long grass. Up and down the path goes until you come to a clearing, now you are able to see the sea, the tide is out, the rock pools are visible and the sand is clean and golden in the sunshine. The beach is empty. You find a sheltered place among the sand dunes where you can sit and watch the changing sea. The grassy bank behind you shelters you from the breeze, this is a quiet, still spot to sit back and relax.

The colour of the sand is golden, and as you allow your fingers to glide through the coarse texture you are mindful of relaxation gently flowing through you. A lone seagull hovers overhead, the movement of the tide gently stirs the rock pools, the steady sound of the waves is comforting, the regular movement of the waves, brings a steady rhythm to your own breathing, and you find yourself drifting, melting into a dream. Gliding and drifting you let go and surrender.

In this dream you can run, dance and skip, you are full of energy, health and free from pain. At the waters edge your bare feet are soothed by the warm water, you allow your ankles and legs to be bathed, you stroll along the waters edge feeling care free, no one is here to watch you now skipping along the waters edge, jumping over a small wave, a

smile, and then a giggle, turns into laughter, how long ago it was since you felt like this, how easy it feels to just be.

Dancing along now you dare the waves to brush your knees, the sand is soft beneath your feet, connecting to the ocean, you feel the energy and the laughter awaken your inner childlike innocence and you celebrate the fact you are alive and well. How well you feel, no aches or pains, just a warm glow of happiness sweeping over you like a wave.

The gentle breeze awakens you, and you stir and look around, all is quiet, all is still, all is well, and you feel so well, lighter, uplifted, and at peace with the world.

Breathing in a Rainbow

This visualisation can be done sitting alone or back to back with a partner.

If you are sitting make sure the back is straight and you are right in the centre of the sits bones. The position is half lotus. If you are back to back with a partner connect yourself to merge with each others energy. Imagine the back as the channel to allow the free flow of Prana or energy. Link into your breath and just witness for a moment your breathing, your heartbeat and any vibrations within the body. Give yourself time to settle into the posture.

Now take the attention to the base of the spine and imagine in this place a globe of coloured light. This globe of light has all the colours of the rainbow within it.

Begin to draw up the colour red, and as it begins to move up the spine repeat to yourself, 'I am drawing up strength', as you draw up the colour red, feel strong. Take this strength right up to the crown of the head.

Return to the base of the spine and begin to draw up the colour orange, as the orange flows up the spine, feel a surge of joy, and repeat to yourself, 'I am filling my life with joy'. Take this joy right up to the crown of the head.

Return to the base of the spine and begin to draw up the colour golden yellow, as the golden yellow flows up the spine, feel the energy pulsating as it fills you with golden energy, repeat to yourself, 'I am filling my body with life force'. Take this energy right up to the crown of the head.

Return to the base of the spine and release the colour green, draw the colour up the spine and allow yourself to feel the relaxation in body mind and spirit. Repeat to yourself, 'I am drawing relaxation, peace and tranquillity into my body'. Take this relaxation right up to the crown of the head.

Return to the base of the spine and draw up the colour violet, feel the soft healing hand of mauve as it gently glides up your spine, and as it moves, repeat to yourself, 'I am healing my body, mind and spirit'. Take this healing right up to the crown of the head.

Now be mindful of this globe of rainbow light which is now at the crown of the head, between the two rainbow globes of light the spine is pulsating with coloured light and energy.

Take a couple of deep breaths and start to allow the colours to flow down the front of your body like a rainbow over a waterfall. As each energy centre is touched you release anything you no longer need to hang onto. This cleansing waterfall of colour washes over you now, bringing strength, joy, energy, peace, relaxation and healing.

Drawing Down the Moon

Complete Yoga Nidra and prepare yourself to go on a journey.

Imagine yourself by the seashore looking up into a dark blue velvet sky. A full moon is shining, throwing a shaft of light onto the dark blue ocean creating a pathway towards the horizon. All is still. As you look at the full moon you notice how round it is, almost the perfect circle tonight. The night is so clear it picks out the halo surrounding the moon, a perfect aura.

As you look into the moon you can see dark and light areas, craters and shapes that change with the light.

Looking into a light area it seems to divide and open, and from this opening comes a shaft of moonlight, moonbeams that seem to flow towards you in a giant shaft of light. They flutter down towards you now glittering and shimmering showering you with silver moonlight and stardust.

The power of the moon is strong, and magnetic. You can almost feel the energy, the draw, as you allow yourself to be bathed in moonbeams and absorbed in light. Allow this light to bathe your body in pure magnetic energy.

As you look towards the full moon the opening begins to close drawing back the shaft of light, drawing back the moonbeams until they become a gentle stream of light and then disappear.

Look into the moon again see the darkening shadows move across as the light changes, the moon moves behind the cloud, the night darkens, the velvet sky deepens and a warm evening breeze draws clouds across the night sky.

The dark blue ocean is still, lit by the light of the moon, gentle waves move the shingle on the seashore, you are in tune with the in and out of the waves, almost in time with your breathing in and out, with a deep even rhythm, You feel your entire body breathing to the sound of the flowing tide, the vibration is the universal sound of O.M. This vibration penetrates to cell level and brings with it balance and equilibrium, it is your perfect pathway to stillness.

Fields of Colour

Imagine you are walking in the country along a wide path on a sunny day. You feel the sun gently warm your back. All is well. On either side of you are open fields, fresh green grass, almost emerald, strong and upright, close your eyes and breathe in the freshness. Breathe in calm.

When you open your eyes on either side of you now are fields of cornflowers, a mass of blue, heads reaching to the sun, bobbing in the gentle warm breeze. Close your eyes and breathe in the delicate shade of summer blue. Breathe in healing.

When you open your eyes on either side of you now are fields of tall upright sun flowers, heads like saucers bathing in the summer sun, close your eyes and breathe in the colour yellow. Breathe in vitality.

When you open your eyes on either side of you now are fields of crimson poppies close your eyes and breathe in the colour red. Breathe in strength.

When you open your eyes on either side of you now are fields of lavender close your eyes and breathe in the delicate shade of mauve. Breathe in stillness.

Now when you open your eyes you have approached a wild meadow full of ox eyed daisies, clovers, buttercups, thistle, and dandelions, a gate leads inside the meadow and on this warm summer day you feel the need to lie down and rest.

The soft grass is comfortable, dry and warm, and you lie down and feel the gentle sun on your face, a skylark sings above, you can hear the gentle rustle of the grasses, your breathing is soft and slow, and your body eases into a deep relaxation, you feel yourself drifting and melting into the sounds of nature, the weaving of the breath in and out, the slow heartbeat, the warm earth supporting you, holding you, and then the silence, the stillness, all you are aware of is your body melting into relaxation. Surrender to the relaxation.

Breathe in the earth, the wild flowers, the skylark and nature in all her splendour. All is well, and all is well.

Walking in Meditation

Imagine you are on a warm sunny tropical beach.

The ocean is azure blue and stretches out to the horizon where it meets the sky. The seamless join between the sky and the ocean.

As you walk along the beach, you are aware of the silence, the stillness, and only the sound of the water gently lapping around your feet. You stop for a moment and admire the beautiful shells just lying where the sea has placed them, how beautiful they are, so intricate and fine, mother of pearl, glistening in the sun.

You begin to feel completely at ease and relaxed. The sound of the gentle waves lapping on the shoreline, in and out exactly like the rhythm of your breath, take you into a deep state of oneness with the ocean, and you can almost hear and sense the vibration of O.M. the universal sound of the universe.

You are now walking in meditation. Your footprints washing away as soon as you make them, your feet are now taking in a new energy from the source of the ocean. How well you feel as you take the ocean into the soles of your feet.

Ahead of you now in the shade, is a small plantation of palm trees. A hammock is strung between two palms and you step inside it. How comfortable you now feel. The coolness is welcome.

In the shade of the palms you allow yourself to completely mould to the hammock, your breathing slows down, you body becomes heavy and you completely let go of weight, you feel yourself drifting and melting into the hammock, the gentle movement takes you into a deep relaxed sleep, and in that sleep, your dreams are o the blue sky, the blue ocean, the moon anc the stars, this wonderful planet of ours and how as beings we are here to experience it so be content, grateful, happy, joyous, and those feelings will bring you success, peace and health.

You want for nothing at all, you need nothing at all, what you have is right here inside you, and always will be, that still small voice that says all is well, and all is well. So relax and allow the deep blue ocean of healing softness wash over you.

Adapted from an idea by Hannah Shine of Bishops Stortford with thanks.

Affirmations With a Posture

Whenever I teach postures I try and build in an affirmation. For instance The Bridge is associated with the element water as it is connected to the Svadishana chakra which is the Chakra of the Abdomen pelvic area. Therefore it is very easy to remember to connect it with water.

The bridge is for strength in the pelvic area.

When I think of affirmations for this posture I would imagine The Bridge over troubled waters and therefore the affirmation, I am building bridges, could mean relationships, or in your personal life you may have to build a bridge, you may have to meet someone half way and bridge the gap, or you may have to cross over, move away or towards, or just link up. The affirmation adds interest to the posture and cements it, if you build up your bridge as you repeat the affirmation.

The Bridge
Now as you go into the bridge posture feel yourself spanning the river, the clear water flowing underneath the spine, clarity and going with the flow. The affirmation could be I am building bridges or I am going with the flow.

The Fish Posture
This posture is again connected with water and is similar to the bridge. The posture works on the heart centre and opens out the chest and shoulders. The fish lives and breathes in water and again in this posture we are creating a bridge and also opening out the chest to create flow, expansion and space, the fish has the freedom to swim everywhere.

With each inhalation open the chest and expand the breath, breathe, build lung capacity and strength, breathe, the bridge spans the river and the fish is freedom. The affirmation is, I am going with the flow of life.

Uddiyana Bandha
Although this is a Bandha I have still used a affirmation, for instance the pull inwards and upwards towards the ribcage is a definite affirmation, I am progressing or I am moving upwards, this Bandha creates a stirring in the abdomen which stimulates the adrenal and naturally stirs the fire in the belly of the Manipura Chakra to give you exactly what you need to move forward and up. It is both liberating and uplifting as well as heat generating.

Lesson Plan on the Four Elements

This is a lesson plan I have used connecting postures to The Four Elements.

Every posture comes with an affirmation and statement, this helps to cement the posture.

Condense to suit time and your own style. 3 Postures one Bandha 10 minute breathing and 20 minute relaxation.

Lesson Plan on the Four Elements.

Earth

The Earth represents grounding, as in having your feet planted firmly. A firm connection to nature and her natural laws, the continual ebb and flow and the circle of life. We work with the colour red when linking to the Muladhara Chakra
The posture is Bhujangasana The Cobra. This posture is for transforming fear into courage.
The attitude of the posture is to create a flow of energy to rise from the base of the spine and as the posture unfolds, increase mobility, this creates the open chest and the freedom and space to breathe.

Go into the posture.

The affirmation is I know no Fear, rising above and transforming fear into strength and courage.

Water

Water is associated with the lower abdomen the Svadishana Chakra, all fluids and liquid are held in this centre. Water symbolises continual flow, movement, creativity, and change. The posture is Setu bandha, The Bridge linked to the Svadishana Chakra.

This posture is for strength in the pelvic area.

When we work with this posture we visualise the colour orange. The attitude of the posture is to go with the flow.

Before choosing the affirmation think of the bridge and what it represents i.e., relationships? You may have to build bridges, to cross over, to move away from, or even to move towards. The Bridge becomes the link to the affirmation.

Go into the posture.

Be aware of your bridge spanning a river and think of the flow underneath, clarity, change and flow.
Therefore your affirmation could be I am going with the flow...

10 minute Breathing to centre

Nadi Sodhana Pranayama

Gather back the Prana for 10 minutes.

Air

Air is connected to the heart centre. We can breathe in to the heart centre to release emotions, feelings, hurt and wounds and we can breathe into the physical heart to release tension, pressure, stress and replace with healing. We visualise emerald green to flood the heart chamber and create harmony and balance. The posture is Matsyasana the Fish linked to the Anahata Chakra.
This posture works on the heart and opens out the chest to the air we breathe. The fish lives and breathes in water, so again in this posture we are creating a bridge and also opening out the chest to create space, room to breathe, expansion, freedom and acceptance.

Go into the Posture

The affirmation is my heart is open to receive.

Fire

Fire is associated with, the Manipura Chakra at the belly. Here the stoking and stirring of emotions and energy, take place. Cleansing and transforming. It is the seat of emotions and connected to all change. For all situations that require strength, purpose and change we need fire in the belly.
This is not a posture but a Bandha a lock or seal. The colour to focus on is yellow.

Uddiyana Bandha

The Lock that lifts up

Uddiyana Bandha creates fire in the belly. The lock is to create a furnace/fire. The churning of the belly creates movement, stirs up the energy to move the Prana upwards hence the lock lifts up.

Prepare and perform the Bandha.

The affirmation is I am progressing and moving upwards.

The White Feather

Go through the usual relaxation technique and begin to feel your self drifting and melting into a safe, calm place. Imagine yourself being surrounded in light. In this glow you begin to feel light, as light as a feather, and you just feel yourself fluttering down exactly like a feather, slowly moving into a safe, warm, comfortable moulded place.

You begin to find yourself walking towards a placid lake on a warm sunny day, the sun is warm on your face and you are feeling good. The sun is glistening and shimmering on the water, and you see before you a group of graceful swans just gently gliding through the calm still water. The scene is tranquil, peaceful and still. The Lake is a very peaceful, quiet place, seldom visited.

A wooden bench is nearby and you sit and watch these graceful creatures, moving through the water, the elegance and stature, close up one swan opens his wings displaying the power of the span, the pure white feathers all in perfect formation, he shakes his head displaying and stretching the length of his neck, the bright orange beak is moving through the water, the strong eyes look towards you, curiously. White swans just gliding and drifting along on a still, quiet, placid lake.

Suddenly as a group they open their wings, glide across the lake, lift up and skim the water creating ripples and a gentle wave. Gliding upwards towards a perfect blue sky they fly away. High up now you see them in formation, a group together, flying in unity, partners for life.

Just beside you on the bench, a single pure white feather flutters past your shoulder to the ground, you reach to pick it up and wonder how such a long, strong feather could possibly have become detached from the swan, the quill being so straight, the feather is soft as down, and contains thousands of tiny feathers each one anchored in place, the feather tapers towards the end, a perfect white feather being given to you as a gift.

Can this feather be a sign, a message?

Feel as though this pure white feather is the sign that you are never alone, that you are now being held by strong white wings, comforted, held tight and embraced, at this moment in time you are home within your heart centre, content, and all is well, and all is well...

The Ocean of Dreams

Imagine yourself lying on a bed of sand. Your body is releasing and melting down into the soft white sand. You feel warm, comfortable and relaxed. The sand is moving and moulding to your body creating a soft bed for you to relax into. Feel the pleasure of just letting go, unwinding, releasing into a safe, warm, and comfortable place.

You feel yourself drifting, and all you are aware of, is the steady movement of the waves rippling on the seashore. Observe the steady movement of the breath just coming and going in harmony to the quiet even rhythm of the gentle waves on the seashore.

Visualise this seashore now, a white tropical sandy beach, a blue ocean, a cloudless blue sky, feel yourself just merging into the colour blue, and somehow without moving you can just dream yourself into the blue tropical ocean.

Dreaming yourself into the warm ocean, you find yourself gliding and floating with the most beautiful tropical fish, shoals of navy blue, bright red, yellow with black stripes, pink spotted, tiny shoals of luminous turquoise, large crimson anemones flutter open and close like miniature umbrellas, golden starfish weave in and out like golden stars, black angel fish moving as a huge dark cloak, red spotted flat fish, the colours and designs are so wonderful.

You pass a bank of bright pink coral, multi coloured fish are darting in and out, every colour you could possibly think of, the light is so bright and clear and the sand pure white, you are able to see every creature moving around the sea floor. Beautiful sea grasses move in waves as if a breeze has caught them, unusual plants plume out with dazzling displays and then close back, disguised as coral.

Now shoals of silver shimmering towards you like a beam of silver light, shoals of dazzling yellow like a beam of sunshine, all moving, turning, gathering, spreading out, and then uniting as one. Natures perfect knowledge.

All around you the ocean is a mass of colourful life and energy, a system living in perfect harmony, just feel at peace drifting along and absorbing these colours.

You dream yourself back onto the white sand, the warmth of the sun, the steady sound of the ocean, the stillness of your breath, the harmony of the universe, the perfect path to peace.

The Silent Glen

Imagine you are beginning a walk up a Glen. The day is fine and warm and you know that this glen leads to a beautiful waterfall. The path is wide and clear and follows a stream, the sun is on your back and all you are aware of, is the sound of the tricking stream as it meanders along. Ahead of you are hills clothed in heather, a deep purple. Mountains, high and majestic rise up in the distance and all around is openness, space, room and freedom that allow you to breathe. You take in a deep inhalation; the air is fresh, cool and pure, full of natural Prana. All around, you are aware of the isolation, the free open path, the natural landscape, the uncluttered skyline, unlimited space.

The path takes you up and the stream becomes more active, the water gushing over stones, creating deep pools, and miniature falls, you stop at a small wooden footbridge, and look up the glen, a deep gorge is ahead and you can hear the thunder of the falls in the distance.

As you walk further you can feel the dampness in the air, the shade, the moss and lichen clinging to the stones, trees overhang the gorge creating shadows. You approach the waterfall, a huge canopy of water is gushing from way high up, sending a shower of spray, and in this spray is a rainbow, the complete spectrum arcing into the side of the gorge. You stop for a while at this spot and just admire the beauty, the waterfall is so powerful, the noise is deafening, a continuous flow of water from the fells above, and you feel invigorated and compelled to visit the source, so you begin to climb the high rugged path each step you take bringing you to the top of the gorge.

Soon you come out onto a sunlit plateau where the fells are bright with purple heather and the mountains are in front of you and the source of the waterfall, a series of gentle streams uniting. And in that unity is oneness.

Ahead of you the path leads over the moor land to a headland and a sandy cove appears, you make your way towards it, a small boat is moored with the boatman ready and waiting to take you back. You get into the boat, you lie back and relax into the sound of the oars brushing the water in deep even strokes, the water is still and placid and you sink into a deep relaxation your breathing in tune to the steady movement. Allow yourself this time to relax and let go into the rhythm of the oars skimming the still placid water.

The Tree of Life

Go through the usual Yoga Nidra and prepare yourself for total relaxation. Imagine that you are sitting beside a lake on a fine summer day. The lake is placid and still, and the sun is shimmering on the water creating a slight heat haze, through the heat haze you are able to make out a small island.

The lake is surrounded by high mountains. All is quiet and still. As you gaze out a slight breeze begins to blow away the heat haze. You sit and gaze for a while and as the haze completely clears you are able to see the island more clearly.

On the island you can see a lone tree, surrounding the tree are bushes laden with deep blue blossom; you can almost smell the perfume.

At the edge of the lake is a small wooden bridge, this bridge takes you over the lake to the small island. The water is very shallow and the bridge is solid and as you walk over the bridge you are able to see the lone tree glinting and glistening, golden leaves are hanging from branches they shine and glint in the sun.

As you come to the end of the bridge you are able to smell the perfume from the blue blossom, this is a flower you have never seen before the blossom hangs like giant globes of blue light.

As you make your way towards the tree you see that the golden leaves glittering in the sunlight have words written on them. You go towards this tree; each leaf is impressed with golden words, comfort, strength, healing, friendship and help.

The tree of life is full of golden leaves each one bearing a positive thought, and you are allowed to borrow whichever leaf you are in need of at this moment in time or you may be thinking of someone else who is in more need than yourself. All the leaves are so bright and you look up into the branches and choose yourself a golden leaf

This tree of life that holds the golden leaves invites you to sit back and relax against the strong trunk. You hold the golden leaf in your hand thinking of the positive thought, hold still, hold fast, and feel the golden light from the leaves surround you as you sit in quiet contemplation.

When you are ready to go, place the golden leaf back on the tree and make your way across the bridge back to the lake side.

You drift back from the visualisation, with the positive thought still clear in your mind.

The Oasis

Prepare yourself for relaxation. Allow yourself to start to relax as if you are lying on a bed of warm golden sand.

Feel the sand mould to your body, you can move around and still feel comfortable. Now allow yourself to just drift with the sound of your breathing, you feel yourself melting down into this soft bed of golden sand, it holds you safe and warm it cannot let you go, so relax and just allow the body to become heavy and solid and release to the moment.

Imagine yourself sitting in the desert beside an Oasis. You are surrounded by palm trees and a small fertile plantation. Camels have come for a drink, birds join them, and a few goats are tethered nearby. This has been a resting place for many travellers.

All around you is sand as far as the eyes can see. Dunes, flat plains and unusual shapes, always moving and shifting, they create a different landscape each new day.

You look into the distance and see a camel trail, a caravan of camels slowly making their way towards the Oasis; they look like a mirage on the horizon. All is stillness and silent.

The sand around you is like fine grain, it moves through your fingers like dust, a beetle moves in the sand creating a ripple, a bird flies in to drink.

The sun is now setting, a ball of orange light draws across the rippling golden desert sand, creating shadows, bursts of light, mirages, until, the sun gently fades, and the sky illuminates to briefly let the red sunset show off its brilliant rays.

The night quickly darkens and you find yourself looking into the indigo velvet sky where the stars are so bright and clear they almost light up the desert, a crescent moon lights up the oasis and night animals come to drink, the palm trees sway with the gentle warm breeze,. The caravan of dusty camels slowly come into the plantation and make for the oasis, this spring of life. After watering they settle into the stillness and tranquillity of this quiet haven in the desert.

Take in the warmth of the desert, the continual shifting sands, the life giving oasis, and the haven of peace.

Mountain Meditation

Imagine you have climbed a high mountain, you have come up a rugged path and ahead of you is a cairn and some smooth moss covered boulders. The day is warm, sunny and clear and you are able to see for miles, the sea in the distance, rolling heather clad hills, stone walls meandering up the hillside, and the gentle sound of a trickling stream as it makes its way down the fells. You sit down against the warm moss covered boulder, it is just the perfect shape for your back. Allow yourself to become comfortable as you ease yourself into a meditation position. Lengthen the back and feel the support of this ancient boulder, how this stone managed to place itself in this position many years ago. Strong and supportive it will now hold you as you allow yourself to let go.

Look around you and feel the stillness, the blue sky, the slow moving fluffy clouds, a butterfly passing, a bird singing, you feel the warm sun on your face as you close your eyes and breathe in the clear mountain air. Feel the chest open and widen to receive the charged prana. Be still, and breathe. Take in the sounds around you, the bird singing, and the soft air around you.

Now draw your self inwards and be aware of the sound of your breath, the slowing down of the heartbeat, relax and let yourself move into a state of deep relaxation, allow the mind to free itself, so that your mind can empty. As thoughts come and go let them move aside to create space in the mind, feel as though you are now clearing out the mind of any perceptions, ideas, judgements, just thoughts moving away and draining from the mind, trickling away until you feel as though you have created a fresh new space.

This new found space will give you the freedom to start afresh, to only create positive thought that will be useful, the mind is now clear, uncluttered and you can keep the clarity until you need to think. You are now in the moment, and in this moment are stillness, peace and balance. Feel the breath slow down as you relax into this new state of awareness. You feel the need to chant OM but you have no need, as you listen carefully you can already hear it in the sound of the trickling stream, the bird song, your silent breath, the boulder you are resting against, and the earth beneath your feet. In this moment you are aware of being part of that universal sound of OM.

Candle Relaxation

For this Meditation the students lie in a circle, head to the centre.

Begin to allow the body to come into a state of complete calm. Be still and centred. Feel the breath moving quietly throughout the body, just witness and observe the movement, the shifting from tension to relaxation, the softness as the body releases, and gives.

In this circle you are connected and so you feel safe and secure. You are linking to the energy of the circle. The circle is linking you to energy. Be aware of the body beginning to settle down, let thoughts flow away.

Encourage your mind to empty, releasing unwanted thoughts, ideas, images, and begin to breathe into your mind now space, exhale clutter, breathe in room, exhale confusion, breathe in emptiness, exhale remaining tension. Now the mind feels free to breathe, you have space, room, and freedom.

Imagine your body is a candle; the spine is the long wick that goes directly to the crown of the head. Take the attention now to the third eye and in this centre visualise a blue candle flame. Directly above your head is a thin watery sun.

This watery sun is now beginning to glow warm, it starts to grow into a ball of warm golden light, and the warmth and heat from these golden rays start to melt the candle. A big round golden sun is now directly overhead.

The blue candle flame is now filling your head with light. The empty space in your head is now filled with light and the glow moves around your neck and shoulders, it cascades down your arms and legs and rolls towards your hands and feet.

You feel yourself melting, drifting, slipping and moving as the candle grease glides, drifts and slides away, it moves over the front of your body like a wave, drips one after the other cascade and roll down the front of your body, warmth and light spreading, as the river of melting wax releases, warms and relaxes your entire body.

Begin to breathe in the stillness, the warmth and light, as the body accepts with each new inhalation waves of relaxation, seeping into the emptiness of your mind, creeping into the fresh places, sliding into new spaces, breathe into your mind the affirmation, my mind is clear.

The mind is now centred in relaxation, in peace, and balanced. The mind is new, fresh uncluttered and ready to receive positive thoughts.

Breathe in the warmth as relaxation rolls down your body, wave after wave, glowing, flowing and melting the wax, taking away anything that you no longer need to hold onto, bringing relaxation and peace.

When you feel ready to come out of relaxation begin to feel the body on your own mat, in this place, solid and physical, remain at peace for a few minutes before getting up.

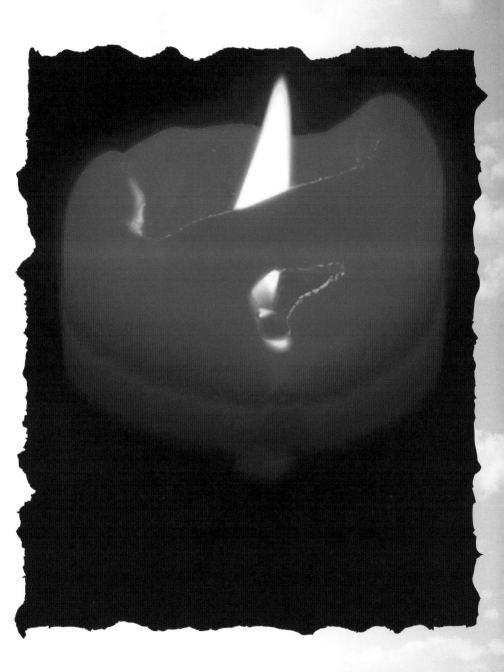

Silence by the Sea

After Yoga Nidra you are ready to go on a journey, a journey into deep relaxation so allow yourself the time and space to completely relax. Feel the whole of your body surrendering to the moment.

This moment is all there is, so try and empty the mind by cultivating space, on an inhalation breathe into that empty space, create room to breathe, on an exhalation release clutter, thoughts, the anxieties of the day, your work, your commitments let everything fall back into the universe.

Breathe in freedom and allow the mind to rest in relaxation, free from thought, in this quiet freedom the mind rests and recovers.

On this journey just listen, and allow the visualisation to take you to deep peace, both mentally and physically, drift into that safe, secure, calm place, where you feel at ease, and as you let go of all your attachments, you now feel lighter, your heart is being welcomed home.

You find yourself sitting beside the sea on a grassy cliff overlooking a sandy cove. A path leads down towards the sandy bay. The day is sunny and bright, the grass is warm and dry, clumps of pink sea thrift turn the cliff tops into a pink blanket. White daisies, buttercups, and clover remind you of childhood daisy chains, and looking for that four-leafed clover.

You lie back on the warm grass, clouds drift by, white and fluffy, pictures take form, shapes appear, and as you day dream you find yourself drifting, the warm sun on your face, the smell of the sea air, sea gulls nesting, the path leading down to the sandy cove, a small boat anchored, the warm sand on bare feet, the shimmering sea, the silence, a lone yacht on the horizon, the sheltered cove, a small rock pool, a sandcastle, a hidden cave, a secret haven of peace and tranquillity.

The breath is now slow and steady, you feel as though the breath is breathing the body, every part of your body is breathing, with each steady inhalation and exhalation, you sense the quiet pulse, rest in this stillness.

Feel the warm sea breeze brush over your face, breathe in the fresh sea air, laden with Prana and life, breathe in positive ions, breathe in this moment and hold it. Begin to bring yourself back from the visualisation, and as you drift back, you feel so energised and yet, you are so relaxed, you are still in the silence, you are still peaceful, you are in the stillness of this moment, and this moment is all there is. All is well, and all is well.

Clearing the Mind

This is an exercise in clearing the mind of all negativity, sometimes we feel overwhelmed by our own thoughts that we need to sit in silence and remove that chattering monkey. This is a good meditation done in a group circle. The practice can start with the clearing and end with a pranayama for instance Nadi Sodhana Pranayama, this practice will help clear and stabilise the mind.

Begin in a circle with a lighted candle in the centre. The idea is to release and let go of all restless, troublesome and invading thoughts, it is important not to intellectualise the thoughts, but allow the thought to be present, and then let them go.

Imagine you are carrying two bags, in one bag are a host of heavy problems, anxieties, and worries, these anxieties may never happen or you may be experiencing them at this moment in time, the point is that the worry and grief are not helpful but are actually hindering healing the mind, so it is important to establish a need for calm and perspective. If something is going to happen it will, and you will deal with it.

This bag of worries holds fear, anxiety, resentment, frustration, bad feelings, greed, ingratitude, and selfishness, anything that at this moment in time is holding you back and interfering with your wellbeing.

The second bag holds all that you wish.

Visualise yourself sitting beside a large open fire; you are ready to open the bag.

Your mind is now calm, ready and focused. You are alone and private with your own thoughts and ideas.

Bring out of the bag that which is bothering you and place it in the fire, watch it burn, it is gone, cleared from your mind and aura. Keep on bringing your worries out of the bag and place them in the fire. As you burn and clear, you begin to feel lighter, as though a burden has been lifted from your shoulders, your neck feels softer, you feel lighter, more relaxed, at ease, breathe a sigh of relief that a blockage has shifted. With each concern gone, you have found balance, equilibrium, and control. This is now a fact.

Now open the second bag, and pull out contentment, peace, gratitude, kindness, happiness, strength, courage upliftment, and joy of life.

You are now focused in your life, you are filled with positive thought, and you are strong, able, and full of energy.

The affirmation is I will live one day at a time. Now cement the practice with Pranayama.

The River

This visualisation is mainly about water so make sure everyone is comfortable before beginning this practice.

Follow the usual Yoga Nidra practice.

Visualise a single drop of water, drips of water, trickling over a stone.
Visualise a stone trough full of water, water trickling over the edge.
Visualise a raindrop, a few raindrops, and a light summer shower.
Visualise rain, a sudden cloudburst, a heavy shower, a downpour, a flash flood.
Visualise the clouds gathering and the rumble of thunder, an electric storm.

Now take the mind back to the raindrop and imagine it turning to snow, falling as soft light crystal flakes, turning into a snow shower, a blanket of snow, visualise a white out as the snow falls thick and heavy.

Now, visualise the snow flakes turning to heavy hailstones of ice, falling and covering the blanket of snow, forming a thick covering of ice, building up layer upon layer of ice until it forms a glacier, hard as the rock, solid as stone.

Imagine a glacier and the trickle of water seeping out at the base, the ice cold water forms a pool of aquamarine dense and opaque, it flows away from the glacier over ancient rocks and boulders and forms a huge river deep and wide rushing along, moving fast, anxious to be away, cutting away the sides of cliff and riverbanks, creating rapids and waterfalls, the noise and spray as the powerful surge of water rumbles along, until finally it gushes over the edge of a gorge and celebrates freedom.

Gathering itself together and relaxing, this mountain of water composes itself and transforms into a beautiful wide river, gently holding the side of the riverbank, releasing into the shape of the river bed, gliding along, experiencing, and owning its flow. This new river of ancient water is now beginning its journey down the mountainside. It tumbles and weaves down the mountain, warms and clears, embraces the newly discovered suns rays and rainbows, and sparkles. Dancing over weirs, singing over rocks and gorges, opening out to freedom, it looks to the full moon, and breathes in more energy.

Many times it stops and relaxes in a quiet still pool, just hearing the sound of its own echo, its heartbeat, the universal sound of o.m.

Breathing in the stillness, listening to the silence, in awe of its own power, it journeys down, meandering over fells, down hills, changing and transforming, dividing and uniting, until it quietly senses change.
The river has turned tidal, and the current and salt of the ocean merge with the river, taking it into the arms of oneness, and in that change is transformation, the circle is complete.

The Summer Show

Visualise yourself in the middle of a large field.

You are walking towards a large Marquee. As you open the canvas door, the smell of roses almost takes your breath away. Inside are tables of flowers and vegetables ready for the show judges. Remember the time you may have spent at a flower show.

The first table holds roses, the old fashioned rose full of perfume, all single stems, they are perfect and just open, visualise a single red rose, a lemon rose, a pink rose, a white rose. Hold the scent, and allow this rose to open out the heart.

The next table holds sweet peas, six sweet peas in a tiny posy, these delicate blooms are just opening, pale cream, apricot, light mauve, pink, all pastel shades. Look at the intricate shape, and how the stem supports such a fragile flower. Hold the scent and feel the emotions rise.

The next table holds pansies, bowls of large flat smiling faces, maroon, purple, deep red, bright yellow spotted, some frilled, double pansies all waiting to be winners. Draw in the healing essence of colour.

The next table holds old fashioned cottage garden flowers. Blue delphiniums, red lupins, white hollyhocks, cream Iris, yellow loosestrife, scented stocks, they bring back memories, and nostalgia hold that emotion.

The next table is showing vegetables, be aware of your senses as you admire fresh home grown tomatoes, a table bursting with goodness, bright red plum tomatoes, small Tom Thumb, giant beef tomatoes, smell the ripeness of the tomatoes still on the vine, breathe in the colour, vitality and freshness.

The next table holds greens, fresh cauliflowers, spring cabbage, firm cucumbers, spinach, all full of health and goodness, still alive fresh from the garden. Breathe in the goodness.

The next table is laden with berries, bowls of wild blackberries, raspberries, strawberries, blackcurrants, bilberries full of juice, gooseberries, fruits of the summer garden, you can feel your mouth watering, visualise yourself now tasting one of those fruits, how it feels, the sweetness and freshness from home grown fruit.

Being surrounded by so much pure energy and colour you feel uplifted and energised. Now go to the table that most appeals to you, the roses? The pansies? The sweet peas? Or the old cottage garden flowers? Maybe the vegetables or fruit.

You now have permission to take whatever you would like, visualise yourself choosing and enjoying this gift.

The Changing Sky

Imagine you are walking along the seashore. You have a spring in your step, walking with a purpose, you welcome the new season of spring, full of expectation, the cycle of the moon brings big seas and the waves pound the shoreline, seahorses and spray, gathering and releasing. The sea is in a hurry, almost out of control to deliver another wave to crash onto the seashore. The power and the sound of the waves, as they pound one after another, drawing away the sand, the shingle the pebbles, altering, shifting, moving and rearranging the shoreline.

Imagine you are lying on a bed of golden sand, the sand moulds, supports and holds your body, you are safe, secure and relaxing. Look up into the big, blue sky on this lazy summer day. All is quiet, still and peaceful. The blue sky stretches far away endless, just shades of blue, pale blue merges with deep blue, changing to almost white as a streak of cloud brushes past. The deep blue sea is still, tranquil and the steady rhythm of the waves as they flow onto the seashore is comforting, relaxing, soothing to the mind and nerves, and draws you deeper into relaxation.

Imagine you are walking along the seashore looking up into a dark autumn sky. The colours have changed, the sky looks broody, stormy, clouds gather and change course, the wind blows the clouds along, and they gather, darkening, waiting, building up, the sky has changed to grey, but somehow the watery sun behind the clouds has created on the horizon a most beautiful late afternoon autumn sunset. Take in that late autumn glow and feel uplifted.

Imagine you are warm and cosy looking up towards a winter sky. The grey sky is heavy and laden with snow. Deep clouds hang overhead promising winter showers. Slow and dark the clouds move along the grey sky, stopping and pausing, The grey clouds hide the winter sun and the wind now rushes the clouds along, bringing darkness and light.

Breathe in security, safety and your warm resting place, you are safe, secure and all is well.

The Boat Trip

Visualise yourself sitting on the cliff tops on a warm summer day. In the distance you can hear the gentle purr of a fishing boats engine. It stops and anchors. Seagulls gather looking for scraps.

A group of racing yachts sail past, sinking into the waves, sails stretched with the breeze. White horses race each other creating plumes of spray. The sea looks almost aquamarine, frothy with the fresh sea breeze, the clouds rush along, the smell of salt on the air, the sun shining, a beautiful summer day.

You lie back on the warm grass, the sun warm on your face, all is well and as you relax you start to drift and daydream. In the distance you hear a gentle humming sound, the small boat is coming towards you, it has your name on the side, the boatman knows you well and you are welcome.

Step inside the boat, you feel safe and secure, you are safe and secure. The boatman takes you around the shoreline and you sit back, and look up at the blue sky, the seagulls nesting on the cliffs, the yachts in the distance, the gentle waves, rocking the boat gently along.

You draw into a sandy cove, a favourite place for gathering shells. Sitting on the warm sand you hold a shell to your ear and hear the sound of the sea.

All is calm, the sea is now like a millpond, the breeze has settled, yachts limp quietly back to harbour, the waves lap on the shore, you sit looking out to sea, in and out, the rhythm of the waves connecting with your breathing, and you find yourself breathing in unison with the waves, as each wave flows in so you inhale, as each wave flows out, so you exhale, until you feel you are at one with the ocean, be aware of yourself now breathing in as the wave draws in, and exhaling as the wave draws out. The breath flows like the waves on the seashore. Waves flowing in and out with rhythm and balance, and your breath flowing steady, deep and even.

Love Yourself

Very rarely do we have time to stop and love ourselves, this is for us.

Imagine you have in your hand a large piece of pink quartz crystal. Pink is related to the heart centre. Begin to breathe deeply and as you inhale take the breath deep into the centre of the chest. With each inhalation feel the whole chest open out, widen and spread, create some room and space. Each breath you take, feel it going deep within, touching your physical heart.

Now visualise yourself placing the pink quartz on your heart centre, and as you take a deep breath, breathe in the colour pink, feel the richness of the pink, the healing properties of crystal, and imagine this crystal now working on the physical heart. The colour pink will now release, unwind and melt away any pressure, any tightness any stress or any emotions that you may be holding on to which may be affecting your heart.

With each in breath confirm with the affirmation, I am opening out my heart centre to receive love unconditionally, I need this love unconditionally, I am worthy of this love unconditionally. I love my heart.

Rest for a moment in the breath and link into any feelings that may arise at this moment in time, do not be surprised by any waves of emotions that may surface, just witness and go with the flow.

Now feel the breath resting in the heart centre, the quietness of the breath, the stillness and breathe deeply.

The source of the pink light rests in the heart centre, soft yet solid, feel the physical heart relaxing, releasing, resting. The rays of pink light are now streaming down your arms and legs, feel the entire body breathing pink, the rays are now spreading throughout your body, bathe in this light. Each cell is receiving, renewing, and bathing in the pink crystal light. Now rest in the breath, the tranquil breath, and repeat your Sankalpa three times. I need this love unconditionally, I am worthy of this love unconditionally, I love you, my rose, my heart.

The Healing Room

After bringing the body and mind into a point of stillness begin the journey to the healing room.

Imagine you are approaching a wooden bedroom door, it is open and you have permission to go inside.

As you open the door you are aware of the sweet fragrance of incense. It is evening and the room is lit by many candles. In the centre of the room is a sumptuous soft bed, covered with a deep navy blue velvet quilt.

The carpet you are walking on is soft blue, and your bare feet sink into the deep pile.

On the bed are three velvet cushions, one emerald green, one pale blue, and one deep purple.

You walk towards the bed it is so inviting, soft and comfortable, it beckons you to lie down, and it is safe to do so. Choose a cushion for your head, the deep emerald green? The deep purple? Or the soft blue. Allow your head to relax into the soft, velvet.

Now feel your body relaxing into the soft comfortable bed, your body is ready for relaxation, feel yourself letting go, this is the time to allow all the stress and strain to drain away, to melt away, feel it slipping and sliding away as you begin to breathe in relaxation. Wave after wave of relaxation is now flowing over your entire body as you melt into the blue velvet quilt.

Now look up to the ceiling and see in the soft candlelight, painted golden moons, suns and stars, they glow and shine down onto

your body, full moons, crescent moons, clusters of stars, shadows pass, and the candle flame flickers, but you are still, at peace, and completely at ease, you feel yourself drifting, and melting into a deep tranquil relaxed state, nothing can disturb your peace.

Your breathing is deep and relaxed. Feel the soft blue velvet quilt holding you and enfolding you in healing blue, feel the light from the golden moon and suns shining down onto you, and do not let the outside world disturb you as you receive this healing.

Meditating on Aum

Some students new to Yoga find chanting a bit embarrassing and they tend to hold back. Sound is a vibration, and energy flows with vibration, therefore it seems a pity to miss out on this practice because of self confidence. Lying down chanting seems strange but you can still get the benefits of chanting whilst lying down when you connect it to a breathing practice.
I call it internal chanting.

Naturally when we breathe in we experience a kind of elevation. Something lifts us up from deep inside, and when we exhale we return to our depth, a deep silence within. It is the movement of the prana, so what we experience is the natural movement of the life force rising and then residing. The inhalation is the movement of the prana and the exhalation is the grounding. Therefore we are working internally.

Introducing a Mantra does mean we have to externalise the practice. A Mantra can be repeated mentally or vocally. Meditating or whispering the sound can still be powerful, it is the connection to the vibration that matters and Aum in whatever form is the vibration of the universal sound.

Now we have to introduce the mantra. In the beginning was the word and the word is Aum. Therefore the universal sound is *Aum*. It is healing to the body mind and spirit, it is calming and it promotes relaxation.

Divide the sound into three parts.
Then silence

Ah sound comes from the abdomen, Oh comes from the heart, or mid chest and um comes from the throat. Then silence.

There are three main chakra points and one continuous flow of sound, the vibration resonates throughout the body through these energy centres.

Lying down we can place the hands on the abdomen and take the inward breath with *ah*, draw it up to the heart centre with *oh*, and exhale with *um*, as in the Ujjayi breath. Then silence. Continuous rounds of O.M lying down will still have the same effect, and help those students who feel a little uneasy about the practice. During the practice lying down, the sound can be either silent or vocal.

I leave it up to the students.

Letting Go of Today

Anidhiya Bhavana is a psychosomatic practice, which is a good therapeutic tool for reviewing and analysing the day's events. This practice could be done before the Yoga class, releasing the day's activities allows the student to focus more on the yoga.

Sit in a comfortable Yoga position concentrating on the breathing for a few minutes. Start to review the day from the very beginning. Do not get into any dialogue with your thoughts just witness the memory of the day. Keep the order of events. Do not judge the events see them as they happened. Start with waking up how you felt mentally and physically. Go through your routine, breakfast, washing and toiletries, the usual domestic routine. Continue through the morning, if you were at work or home. Stopping for lunch, shopping, appointments, jobs that had to be completed, visits to make. Afternoon, trips, work, shopping, preparing and making meals, childcare, homework, the evening meal, how you managed to get here.

Now how do you feel mentally and physically as you review the day, did you worry about anything? and is it so bad now the event has passed? If you were concerned about today, now that it is nearly over, how have you coped? How have you managed that problem, that appointment, it is behind you now, so you are strong. The actions of today are part of your character, so you have learnt a lesson from today to help you with tomorrow. Each day brings lessons which strengthen our mind and allow us to grow. Would you have lived today any other way?

Let the day go now as you allocate it to your memory, breathe, and as you breathe feel the new space, openness, emptying your mind of muddle and clutter, let it flow away, roll away, as you draw in a fresh mind, a fresh start, a clear head, room to just be, to be still, to be in a open space that allows you to breathe mentally, with each inhalation feel the clearing, the cleansing, the brushing away, as relaxation now flows into your mind.

In this clear and open space which is your mind, you now have a fresh new day ahead, be still and realise that the mind is only your thoughts in transit. Now you are completely at ease and relaxed, how do you feel?

Rapid Visualisation

Lie in your comfortable relaxation position and feel yourself lengthen and widen. Allow your body to surrender. The earth will support you. Be aware of your breathing, feel the belly rise and fall with each inhalation and exhalation. Come into your calm centre, you are beginning to feel warm, at ease and still.

Be aware of all the outside noise and then take your attention inwards, hear your heartbeat, the rhythm of the breath, any internal vibrations. Do not allow yourself to become disturbed. You feel yourself sinking, releasing, and melting into complete relaxation.

Imagine you are lying on a bed of golden sand, the sand holds and supports you, all aches and pains melt and flow away. Feel the sun warm and soothe you, the gentle breeze cool you, as you drift.

Now visualise your self in a courtyard there is a pond. The pond is still. Goldfish in the pond. Water lilies. A lotus leaf. A Buddha statue nearby.

A group of monks in saffron robes walking. Bells ringing. Prayer wheels. Praying hands. A temple. The open temple door.

Allow yourself to go through the temple door, the air is filled with the strong smell of incense, monks are praying and chanting, prayer wheels are turning, a monk guides you to sit on a cushion, he places around your neck a garland of flowers, marigolds, and rose, you inhale the strong perfume.

Sit for a while and take in the peace and reverence.

Chakra Meditation

Begin by sitting well and use the Hridaya Mudra. Open out the shoulders, and chest. Begin by settling into the breath allowing the mind to empty. Take the inhalation into the heart centre, into the physical heart and feel the exhalation travel down the front of the body back to the earth.

With each inhalation increase the awareness in the heart centre. Breathe in the elevation of the breath and release to the earth. When you begin to notice the change in how you are feeling rest in the breath for a few minutes.

Now take the inhalation to the forehead, and as you exhale, release the breath down the front of the body visualising the breath touching each energy centre back to the root centre.

Now take the inhalation to the throat, and as you exhale, release the breath down the front of the body visualising the breath touching each energy centre back to the root centre.

Now take the inhalation to the heart centre, and as you exhale, release the breath down the front of the body visualising the breath touching each energy centre back to the root centre.

Now take the inhalation to the belly and as you exhale, release the breath down the front of the body visualising the breath touching the remaining energy centres.

Now take the inhalation to the sacral area and as you exhale, release the breath into the last energy centre.

Now breathe into the root centre and exhale to the earth.

Now the body is completely calm and each energy centre has been stirred.

Now bring some balance and healing into the chakras.

Breathe into the forehead and visualise the colour Indigo, allow the colour to flood into this centre and rest in meditation.

Breathe into the throat and visualise the colour blue, allow the colour to bathe the throat and neck and rest in stillness.

Breathe into the heart centre and visualise the colour green, allow the colour to fill the chest and rest in peace.

Breathe into the belly and visualise the colour yellow, allow the colour to completely surround the abdomen and rest in energy.

Breathe into the sacral area and visualise the colour orange, allow the colour to completely fill your pelvis and glow with joy.

Breathe into the root centre and visualise the colour red, feel the colour surrounding your lower back and feel the strength.

Now you are aware of the vibration of all these colours merging, uniting, opening and unblocking, creating within us channels for energy to flow unimpeded.

Four Seasons in the Woods

Imagine you are in the woods on a cold, crisp winter's day; the earth beneath your feet is cold, hard and frozen solid. Branches crackle and splinter. Frost clings to leaves creating mosaic patterns, the trees are bare. The earth sleeps. All is quiet. The trickling stream is stilled by frozen ice. The cold steel sky is full of snow. Your breath is warm against the cold air. Walk in silence.

Imagine you are in the woods on a spring morning, the first buds are forming on the bare trees, you can hear the gentle sound of a trickling stream, the smell of wild garlic fills the air, clumps of bluebells are emerging, the woods are busy, the early sun is filtering between the trees, the light is clear, breathe in the new energy. Walk with anticipation.

Imagine you are walking in the woods on a bright summer day, the earth is dry beneath your feet, the trees are full of leaves, bushes of yellow gorse, hawthorn and wild dog rose fill the air with scent, birds fly in and out of the trees, all is green, fresh and new, the sun shines through and the woods are full of light. Walk with joy.

Imagine you are walking in the woods on an autumn day. The earth beneath your feet is soft and damp with fallen leaves. The trees are copper brown almost bare, cobwebs weave between trees, glistening, branches dusty and dry crackle beneath your feet, berries are forming, the wood seems darker, the days are shorter, the light is weaker, the time for rest and renewal is near. Breathe in the air of a departing season and walk with faith.

The Rainbow Pool

Begin this meditation by sitting well. Place the hands in Hridaya Mudra. This opens out the heart centre. Spend a few minutes connecting to your breathing. Feel the mind beginning to still, and settle. Take the attention to the centre of the forehead, and start to create some space. Feel a widening in the centre of the forehead, creating a widening in the mind. As you continue to breathe allow yourself to empty mentally and physically. Just be in the moment. You can now feel yourself relaxing preparing for the meditation.

In front of you is a pool of water, ripples pass in and out from the centre and then begin to settle like your mind, until the pool is now calm and still. Look into the pool and see the clearness, the water is crystal clear. A rainbow of colour now suspends over the pool, this rainbow is being absorbed into the clear water just for you, it brings all the healing light you need at this moment in time. As you gaze into the water you feel the healing light wash over you. Sit for as while.

Now visualise the sun shining onto the pool, the sun mixes with the strands of colour and you are bathed in sunshine and colour. Sit for a while.

Now visualise darkness, a full moon is now reflected in the pool. All you can see is the light shining on the pool. Breathe in the magnetic strength and energy of the full moon and feel it wash over you. Sit for a while.

Now as you look into the pool it is crystal clear and you can see your reflection, how relaxed you feel, completely at ease. Sit for a while and enjoy the stillness, and the silence.

Hridaya Mudra

The heart gesture. In this Mudra join tip of thumb, middle and ring finger together, the little finger remains straight. The first finger curls in. Place the hands on the knees palms facing up. The physical awareness on the breath is in the chest area, the Anahata chakra. This Mudra diverts the flow of prana from the hands to the heart.

Christmas Meditation

This simple meditation can help us to use the Christmas tree as an expression of peace and healing for the entire planet. In the Yoga Class we can also sit in a circle with lighted candles.

Christmas Meditation

Imagine a forest of Pine Trees shining pure emerald green on a cold winter day.

The Fir tree is bright emerald green as it shines in the winter sunshine, strong and upright it breathes in light and energy, it spreads her branches and just reaches out. The forest of fir trees is a mass of energy, waiting in the deep snow. Avenues of trees, waiting. The cones clinging to the branches, icicles hang, dripping in the winter sunshine. Cobwebs glisten as the mist and rain fail to destroy their intricate design. The strong smell of pine is carried on the silent cold wind. The Fir tree reaches up towards the light and breathes, the plantation is ready, each Fir tree grown especially to be decorated.

Visualise this tree coming into your home and dress it with dignity. Think of dressing this tree with the colour blue and silver, blue for healing the planet and silver for light to shine all around the planet. Dress the tree with the sole purpose of creating peace and light. As it spreads out the branches and gives unconditionally, so place the brightest and largest star on the tip of the highest branch, this is the star of faith, hope and charity.

On each outspreading branch place a blue ball of light, fill the whole tree with silver and blue, and see the light radiating from each branch. Each time you look at the tree you are reminded of the healing and peace radiating, your home is filled with light and healing, and so the aura you live in will also be calmed. Each time you breathe in you are aware of pine, forest and bark, the air is charged with energy, the colour green is peaceful, soothing on the nerves, and harmonious.

By bringing the tree into your home this Christmas time you are sending a message of peace and healing around the planet. Sit for a while and look at the tree and allow your thoughts to travel the world.